QUIZ WHIZ NATURE

QUIZ WHIZ
NATURE

KINGFISHER

KINGFISHER

First published 2010 by Kingfisher
an imprint of Macmillan Children's Books
a division of Macmillan Publishers Limited
20 New Wharf Road, London N1 9RR
Basingstoke and Oxford
Associated companies throughout the world
www.panmacmillan.com

ISBN 978-0-7534-3021-7

Copyright © Macmillan Children's Books 2010
Produced for Kingfisher by Toucan Books Ltd

9 8 7 6 5 4 3 2 1
1TR/0510/WKT/UNTD/140MA

A CIP catalogue record for this book is available from the British Library.

Printed in China

Contents

How to use this book

Read all about it first! Start with the introduction and follow the boxes across the pages from left to right and top to bottom. Look at the pictures, too, because sometimes the answers can be found there. Then it is time to tackle the questions...

1. Eight questions

The questions are on the far left. In addition to general questions, there are true or false options and sometimes you have to unjumble letters to find the answer!

2. Follow the numbers!

All the answers are somewhere on the page. If you do not know the answer straight away, each question has a matching number in a coloured circle to help you find the right place to start reading.

3. Find the answer

When you have answered all the questions, turn to the back of the book and see if you were right!

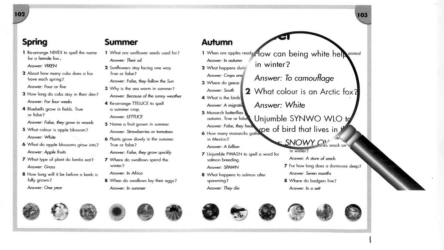

Chapter one
HABITATS

Rainforests

A rainforest grows where it is warm and also very wet. These forests are home to more living things than anywhere else on Earth.

1 Where do ocelots hunt in the rainforest?
tree branches

2 Unjumble GARAJU to spell the name of a big jungle cat.
JAGUAR

3 What is the loudest animal in the rainforest?

4 For how long can a macaw live?

5 When do army ants make camp?

6 Who guards an army ant queen?

7 In what part of the world do poison dart frogs live?

8 Is it safe for other animals to eat a poison dart frog?

Jungle cats 1 2

Rainforests are full of cats. Smaller cats, such as the ocelot, hunt in the tree branches. The jaguar (below) is much bigger. The blotches on its fur help the cat hide in the shadows.

Life in the trees ③ ④

A rainforest is a crowded place – and it is noisy! The loudest animal of all is the howler monkey. Males make hooting calls that can be heard up to five kilometres away. Large parrots called macaws also squawk very loudly. Macaws can live for up to 75 years.

On the march ⑤ ⑥

Army ants do not have a fixed nest. Instead they keep moving around and make a camp each night. Thousands of ants march along, carrying their queen and her eggs. Soldier ants with big biting jaws guard the queen.

Poisonous skin ⑦ ⑧

The forests of Central and South America are home to poison dart frogs. Their colourful skin warns other animals that the frogs are poisonous to eat.

Temperate forests

The word temperate is another way of saying "mild". Temperate forests grow where the weather is seasonal.

1 What colour is the forest's main hunter?

2 What does a jay do in autumn?

3 Where does a badger live?

4 Re-arrange MELAP to spell the name of a forest tree.

5 Deciduous trees keep their leaves all year around. True or false?

6 What colour do the leaves change to in autumn?

7 Why do leaves go brown before they fall off?

8 Where do koala bears live?

Woodland animals 1 2 3

A A red fox is the main hunter in the forest.

B A jay buries nuts in autumn.

C A wild boar is one of the most dangerous animals in the forest.

D A goshawk swoops on small mammals and birds.

E A grey squirrel scurries up and down tree trunks.

F Red deer are some of the largest forest animals.

G A beaver gnaws at a tree trunk.

H A badger lives underground.

D

A

B

C

oak

beech

4

willow

maple

Deciduous trees **5**
The easiest way to identify a tree is to look at the shape of its leaves. Most of the trees in a temperate forest are deciduous. That means they have wide, flat leaves, which fall off every autumn. New leaves grow in spring.

E

F

H

Changing colour **6 7**
In autumn the leaves in the forest change colour from green to brown. This happens because the leaves stop producing a green pigment, chlorophyll, which is used by them to capture energy from sunlight. As a result, the brown or red pigment becomes more visible.

In Australia **8**
The temperate forests of Australia are home to unusual animals, such as koala bears. Koalas eat the leaves of eucalyptus trees.

G

Taiga forests

The largest forests in the world are taiga forests. They grow in cold northern areas of the world where the ground is covered in snow for half the year.

1 Most taiga forest trees are evergreen. True or false?

2 What shape are the leaves of trees in taiga forests?

3 Name four types of food eaten by brown bears.

4 What colour is a squirrel living in taiga forests?

5 How does a woodpecker make a hole in bark?

6 What colour is a timber wolf?

7 Unjumble YNXL to name a wild cat.

8 Why do lynx need large paws?

Taiga life   **1 2 3**

The trees in a taiga forest are mostly evergreen conifers. They have needle-shaped leaves that stay on the tree all year round. The largest hunters in the taiga are brown bears. They eat roots, fungi and berries, and hunt fish.

brown bear

In the trees 4 5

Red squirrels are the most common squirrel in taiga forests. Black woodpeckers hammer holes in tree bark with their sharp beaks, and eat the ants and other insects living in the wood underneath.

red squirrel

black woodpecker

Timber wolf 6

The grey wolves living in taiga forests are known as timber wolves. They work together in packs to hunt large animals.

Wild cat 7 8

Lynx live alone, deep in the taiga forest. They hunt at night and sleep during the day. Their paws are large to help them walk on snow.

Deserts

Some deserts do not get any rain for many years. With so little water, it is difficult for plants and animals to survive.

1 Unjumble ASIOS to name a desert area with a water supply.

2 Where does the water in an oasis come from?

3 Where is the Sahara Desert?

4 A mountain desert is always hot. True or false?

5 What does the wind do to the rocks in a desert?

6 Where does a cactus keep water?

7 Why does a fennec fox hunt at night?

8 What type of animal is a sidewinder?

At the oasis ① ②
A desert area with a supply of water is called an oasis. The water comes from rivers deep under the ground. Green palm trees grow around the oasis.

Hot and cold ③ ④

Many deserts are in hot parts of the world, such as the Sahara Desert in Africa. Others are dry because a wall of mountains stops rain reaching the area. Mountain deserts get very cold in winter.

Worn away ⑤

Deserts are very windy. The dry, sandy air blasts against the rocks, making them wear away, or erode. Eroded rocks may have strange shapes.

sidewinder snake

fennec fox

cactus

Survival ⑥ ⑦ ⑧

Desert life must stay cool and save water. Cactuses store water in their wide stems. Fennec foxes sleep in the day and hunt at night, when it is cooler. The sidewinder snake moves sideways over the sand to keep cool.

Tundra

The tundra is a very cold and empty place for most of the year. However, in the short summer the tundra bursts with life.

1 The tundra is hot all year round. True or false?

2 What kind of plants grow on the tundra?

3 Unjumble NSOYW WOL.

4 What do many tundra birds feed their chicks?

5 At what time of year do reindeer live on the tundra?

6 What do reindeer do in the winter?

7 Where is most of the world's tundra?

8 What grows on mountain tundra?

Icy Arctic landscape   **1 2**

The tundra's soil is always frozen. Only the top thaws in the summer. There is no room for deep roots, so only small plants grow there.

geese

Tundra birds   **3 4**

In summer, the tundra is filled with insects and many birds, such as grouse and geese. They feed insects to their chicks. Snowy owls live on the tundra all year round. They hunt for voles and mice.

snowy owl

Tundra deer 5 6

Reindeer live on the tundra in large herds and graze on its plants during the summer. In winter, the deer move to the forest for shelter; here, they forage for food under the snow.

In the mountains 7 8

Most of the world's tundra is near to the North Pole, but it is also found on high mountains where it is very cold. In summer, the mountain tundra is filled with low-growing plants and grasses. In winter, the ground is covered in snow.

grouse

Mountains

The tops of the world's highest mountains reach eight kilometres into the sky. The air up there is so thin that it is hard to breathe.

1 What is the top of a mountain called?

2 Where is Mount Everest?

3 What is a river of ice on a mountain called?

4 What do glaciers do to rocks?

5 Mountain plants are always very big. True or false?

6 Re-arrange BSOWNELL to spell a type of mountain flower.

7 Where do ibex goats live?

8 Why do ibex grow thick fur?

Mount Everest

High peaks 1 2

Mountains are high, steep-sided hills. The top of a mountain is called its summit – the world's highest peak is Mount Everest in the Himalayas, Asia.

horn

cirque

moraine

Rivers of ice   3 4

Some mountain valleys have a glacier – a river of ice that moves downhill very slowly. As it slides, the glacier grinds away at rocks. At the bottom, the glacier melts and feeds a river or lake.

crevasse

meltwater lake

edelweiss

Snow flowers   5 6

It is very cold and windy on top of mountains, and the plants that grow there are very small. Snowbells (right) poke through the ice in spring.

snowbells

marmot

Tough animals   7 8

Marmots are large squirrels. They survive the winter by sleeping in burrows. Ibex goats live in the mountains of Africa, Europe and Asia. They have wide feet for climbing on rocks. Their fur is thick for keeping out the cold.

ibex

Volcanoes

A volcano is a hole in Earth's crust. Hot, melted rocks from deep inside Earth flood out of the volcano. Most volcanoes are tall mountains.

1 Earth's surface is moving. True or false?

2 Where do most volcanoes form?

3 Re-arrange LATOL to spell a type of coral island.

4 In what type of seas do atolls form?

5 What is hot, liquid underground rock called?

6 At what point does magma become lava?

7 What shape is a common volcano crater?

8 What happens when lava cools?

Moving plates 1 2

Earth's surface is made of moving plates. Volcanoes can form where these plates are pushing past each other under mountains. Volcanoes are also found where plates are splitting apart under the ocean.

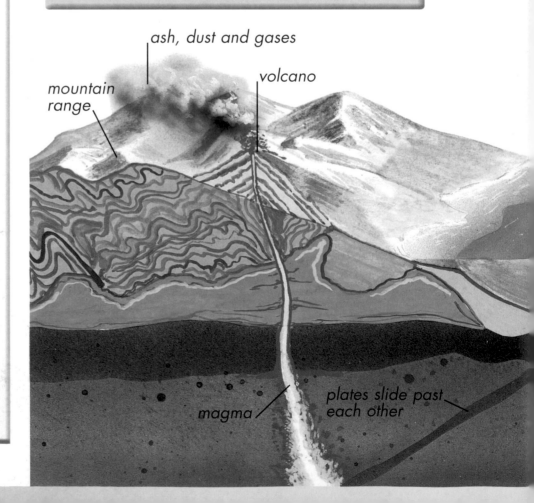

ash, dust and gases

volcano

mountain range

magma

plates slide past each other

Atolls **3 4**

In warm seas, volcanic islands have coral growing around them. Eventually, the volcanic rocks are worn away. All that is left is a ring of coral, called an atoll.

coral reef

atoll

1

volcanic island *2*

3

Cone-shaped **7 8**

Many volcanoes have a round, cone-shaped crater at the top. They are made from layers of lava that have cooled to form rock.

Lava **5 6**

The hot, liquid rock deep underground is called magma. This changes to lava as it spurts out of the volcano. Lava flows down the mountainside.

cracks in sea floor

volcanic island

Swamps and marshes

Swamp and marsh are common names for wetland. They are soggy places where shallow water covers the ground all year round.

1 Why are most plants unable to grow in a swamp?

2 Where do swamp cypress trees grow?

3 Where can you see Spanish moss?

4 Re-arrange GATIALLRO to make a type of swamp animal.

5 Where does a mangrove forest grow?

6 Mangrove tree roots stick out of the soil. True or false?

7 Where do gallinules walk?

8 What do wetland birds eat?

Swamp plants 1 2 3
The soil in a swamp is mainly underwater and very wet. Most plants cannot grow there as they would drown. Swamp cypress tree trunks grow out of the water; Spanish moss hangs from branches.

swamp cypress

Spanish moss

alligator

Mangroves 5 6

Forests growing in swamps beside the sea are called mangroves. When the tide goes out, the tree roots poke out above the ground. The roots have tiny holes in them for taking in the oxygen the plants need.

great blue heron

roseate spoonbill

Bird life 7 8

Wetlands are a good place to see birds. The gallinule walks on floating lily pads. Other birds, such as spoonbills, have long legs for wading in the water. They feed on fish, insects and shellfish.

American purple gallinule

Ponds and lakes

A lake is the same as a pond, only much larger. Their water comes from rivers or springs. Some ponds and lakes are very deep.

1 What do great diving beetles eat?

2 What is the name for a baby dragonfly?

3 Re-arrange NERMOOH to spell a lake bird.

4 What do beavers use to build a dam?

5 What does a beaver eat?

6 What do tadpoles grow before they become frogs?

7 Name a type of lake fish.

8 Most perch have red fins. True or false?

Pond animals 1 2

These animals live in ponds and rivers: Moorhens nest in the plants next to the water. Mallard ducklings spend several months following their mother. Common frogs dive into water to get away from danger. Great diving beetles hunt for baby insects. Naiads are baby dragonflies. Adult dragonflies climb up water plants when they are ready to fly away. A crested newt spends its whole life in the water.

moorhen

3

A

B

C

mallard duckling

common frog

Making a dam **4 5**

Beavers create their own lakes by building a dam across a river out of logs. They use their sharp teeth to gnaw through tree trunks and then float the logs into place across the river. The beavers feed off plants, as well as bark from logs.

Life cycles **6**

A Frogs lay their eggs in ponds.
B The eggs hatch into tadpoles, which live in the water.
C The tadpoles grow legs and turn into adult frogs that can live on land.

Fish **7 8**

Lakes and ponds are full of freshwater fish, including perch (below), carp and pike. Most perch are dark green with red fins, and can weigh up to three kilos.

dragonfly

great diving beetle

naiad

crested newt

perch

Rivers

Rivers carry water from the mountains to the sea. Most river water is rain that has trickled off the land. Other rivers are fed by melting snow or springs that gurgle up from underground.

1 Where do capybaras live?

2 How long is the world's largest rodent?

3 What is a river's source?

4 Where would you find an estuary?

5 Crocodiles and caimans are frightened of water. True or false?

6 What is an anaconda?

7 Do electric eels live in rivers?

8 Re-arrange HANAPRI to spell a type of river fish.

Giant rodents   1 2

Rivers in South America are home to capybaras, the world's largest rodents. Most rodents, such as mice, are tiny animals. A capybara is more than one metre long!

capybara

lungfish

caiman

angelfish

brown discus fish

A river's course 3 4

The start of a river is called its source. Near the source, the river is narrow and flows quickly down steep slopes. On flatter land, the river slows down and gets wider. It also makes large turns. The river mouth, or estuary, is where the river's water mixes with seawater.

snow

lake

waterfall

flood plain

estuary

Reptiles 5 6

Crocodiles and caimans are expert river hunters. They lurk in shallow water before grabbing prey from the bank. The world's largest snake, the anaconda, lives on South America's rivers.

anaconda

8

piranha

electric eel 7

Rock pools

When the tide goes out, seawater left behind in hollows forms rock pools. Many animals wait in these pools until the tide comes back in.

1 Limpets are not related to snails. True or false?

2 How do scallops move around?

3 Unjumble the word LLEJYSHFI to spell the name of a stinging animal.

4 What stops crabs from drying out in the air?

5 What are a crab's gills for?

6 Crabs have four legs. True or false?

7 How many pincers does a crab have?

8 Where do most rock pool animals live?

Animal life ① ② ③

A Limpets are related to snails. Their shells grow to fit the rock.
B Blennies are little fish that scrape food from the rocks.
C Pipefish.
D Scallops move by squirting a jet of water from their shells.
E F Starfish (E) and sea urchins (F) both have mouths underneath their bodies and graze on seaweed.
G The rock goby eats small crabs, shrimps and other fish.
H Jellyfish have stingers. Don't touch!

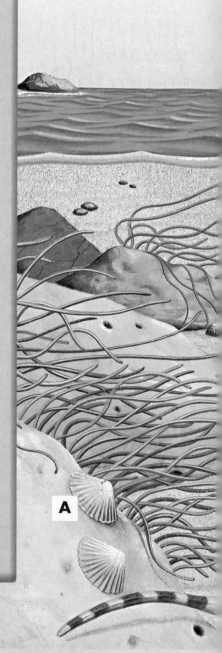

A

Rock walker 4 5

Crabs feel at home in rock pools. They can walk in and out of the water. Their shell stops them drying out in air. They breathe with gills, which work underwater and out of it.

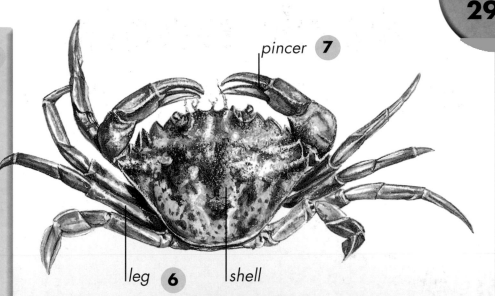

pincer 7

leg 6   *shell*

Changing water 8

Most animals live in the pools nearest to the sea. The water in the rock pools higher up the shore is too warm and salty for them.

B

C

D

E

F

G

H

Coral reefs

Coral reefs are like gardens in the ocean. They are full of colour and many animals live in them, including shrimps, octopuses and snakes.

1 How do some reef fish eat corals?

2 What type of eel lives in coral reefs?

3 Do sharks ever visit coral reefs?

4 What does a sea turtle eat?

5 There is a type of turtle called an eaglebeak. True or false?

6 Corals are a type of animal. True or false?

7 Unjumble POPYL to spell another word for coral.

8 What lives inside some coral polyps?

Reef fish

1 **2** **3**

The fish living in coral reefs are very colourful. Some eat corals by scraping them from the rocks. Big fish, such as moray eels and sharks, are hunters, and are always nearby.

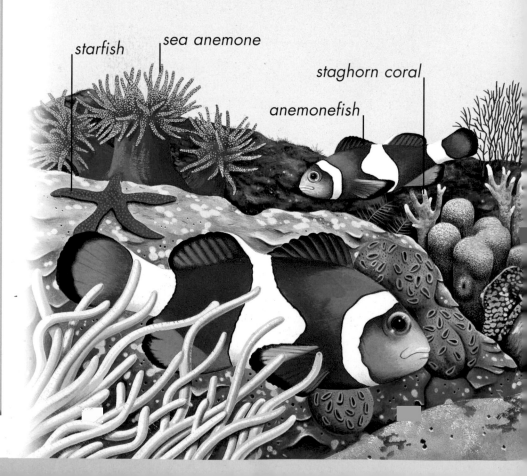

starfish

sea anemone

staghorn coral

anemonefish

Wanderer 4 5

Sea turtles visit reefs to look for shellfish to eat. They stay for a few days before heading out to sea. This hawksbill turtle (left) gets its name from its bony mouth, which is hooked like a hawk's beak.

Living rocks 6 7 8

Coral is a type of animal, not a plant or a rock. A coral reef has billions of coral polyps, which are tiny relatives of jellyfish. Each polyp has arms, called tentacles, that surround its mouth. Some have tiny plants called algae growing inside them.

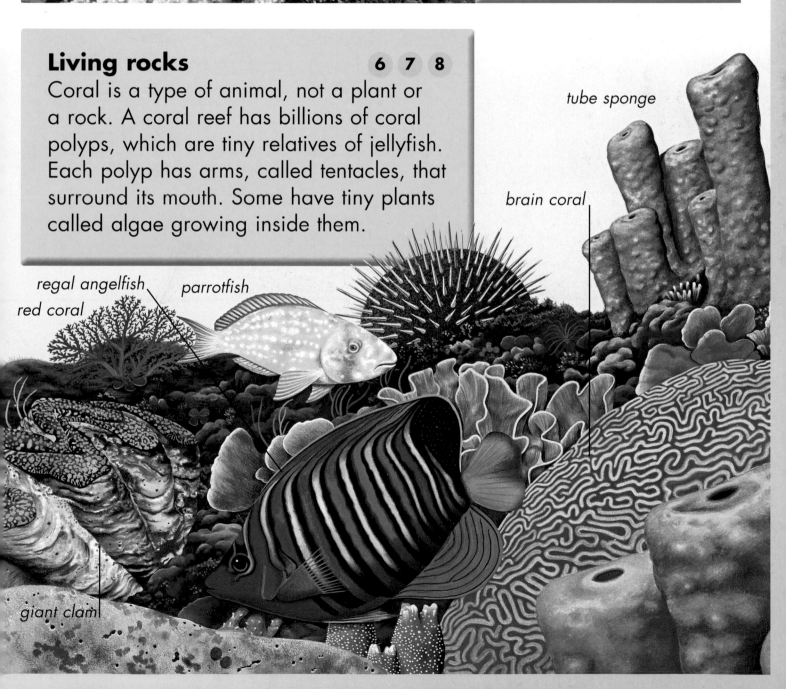

tube sponge

brain coral

regal angelfish

red coral

parrotfish

giant clam

Deep sea

The deep ocean is as dark as night – even when it is daytime on the surface. No sunlight reaches deeper than 1,000 metres under the waves.

1 How do some deep-sea animals make their own light?

2 Name one reason for making light in the deep sea.

3 Jellyfish bodies are hard. True or false?

4 How does a jellyfish trap prey?

5 What do jellyfish stingers fire?

6 Unjumble QDUIS to spell a deep-sea giant.

7 Is a giant squid as long as a bus or a train?

8 How many people have seen a giant squid alive?

Lights on 1 2

Some deep-sea animals have to make their own light using chemicals in the skin. The lights are used to trick prey, scare away attackers or to attract mates.

Stingers   3 4 5

Jellyfish have very simple bell-shaped bodies. There are no hard parts at all. They float through the sea trapping fish and other prey with their tentacles. Jellyfish kill prey by firing poison from their stingers.

Spineless giant   6 7 8

The deep sea is home to the largest invertebrates of all. (Invertebrates are any animals without a spine, or backbone.) Giant squids grow as long as a bus and are real-life sea monsters. But no one has seen one alive.

The Poles

The Poles are cold regions at the top and bottom of the planet. At the Poles it is dark all winter and light for 24 hours a day in summer.

1 What is the name for the area around the North Pole?

2 What covers most of the Arctic?

3 Name an animal that lives on the Arctic ice.

4 Unjumble PLARO EARB.

5 Where is Antarctica?

6 How do emperor penguins stay warm in winter?

7 How wide are albatross wings?

8 What does an albatross use its long wings for?

Arctic life

1 2 3

The area around the North Pole is known as the Arctic. Most of the Arctic is covered by an ocean, which is frozen for much of the year. Arctic animals live on the ice. They include seals and walruses. Polar bears hunt for these animals on the ice.

Asia

Arctic

North America

Arctic tern

4

polar bear

Antarctic life **5** **6**

The land around the South Pole is called Antarctica. Animals such as sea lions live along the coast. Few animals live on the land. Emperor penguins (right) are the only animals to stay all winter. They huddle together to keep warm.

Wandering albatross **7** **8**

The albatross has the largest wingspan of any bird. Its wings are three metres across! The albatross can glide around the Antarctic for hours as it hunts for squid.

gull

Arctic skua

albatross

killer whale

sea lion

HABITATS
Record breakers

1. The deepest part of the ocean is Challenger Deep in the Pacific. The seabed is 10,911 metres below the surface.

2. The largest swamp in the world is the Pantanal in Brazil, South America. It is twice the size of Iceland.

3. Mount Etna in Italy is the most active volcano in the world. It has erupted continuously for 3,500 years!

4. The largest coral reef is the Great Barrier Reef near Australia. At 2,012 kilometres long, it can be seen from space.

5. The Amazon River in South America is the longest in the world. It measures 6,516 kilometres.

6. The coldest temperature ever recorded was −89.2°C in Antarctica in 1983.

7. The world's largest freshwater lake is Baikal in Russia. It contains a fifth of all the freshwater on Earth's surface.

8. The highest country on Earth is Lesotho in Africa. Its lowest point is 1,830 metres above sea level.

9. The world's highest sand dune is Cerro Blanco in Peru. It is 2,070 metres tall.

10. A third of all trees grow in taiga forests.

Chapter two
WEATHER AND CLIMATE

Sunshine

Almost all of the light that hits Earth comes from the Sun. The only other light we can see comes from stars millions of kilometres away. Earth goes around the Sun once every year.

1 Sunshine warms Earth. True or false?

2 What do plants use sunshine for?

3 How often does the Sun rise and set?

4 Unjumble SXIA.

5 Are the Poles warmer than the equator?

6 What is the Sun made of?

7 How long does it take for sunshine to reach Earth?

8 The surface of the Sun is called the photosphere. True or false?

Energy giver   1 2
Sunshine warms Earth. Without it everything would be frozen – even the air! Sunlight also fuels all life on Earth. Plants use the energy in sunshine to help make their food.

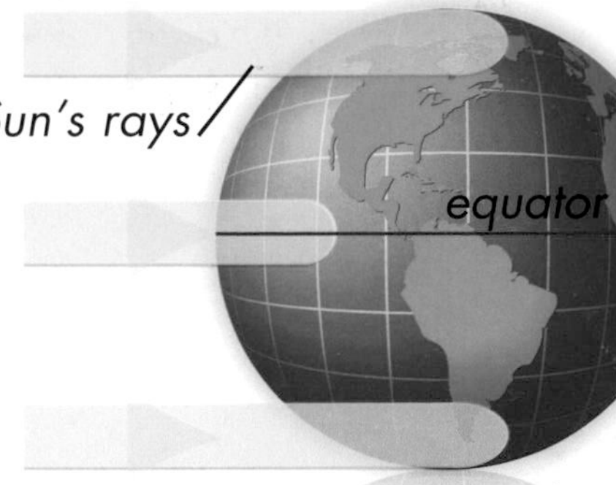

North Pole

Sun's rays

equator

South Pole

Sun

axis

Earth

direction
of rotation

Hot rays 3 4 5

The Sun rises and sets each day as Earth spins on its axis. Days are colder near the Poles because sunshine is spread over a wide area. At the equator, half way between the Poles, sunshine is always strong.

Inside the Sun 6 7

The Sun is a ball of hot gas. All the Sun's light and heat start out in the core, where the gas atoms are squeezed very hard. The energy slowly moves outwards. It takes years to reach the surface, but the sunshine then takes just eight minutes to arrive at Earth.

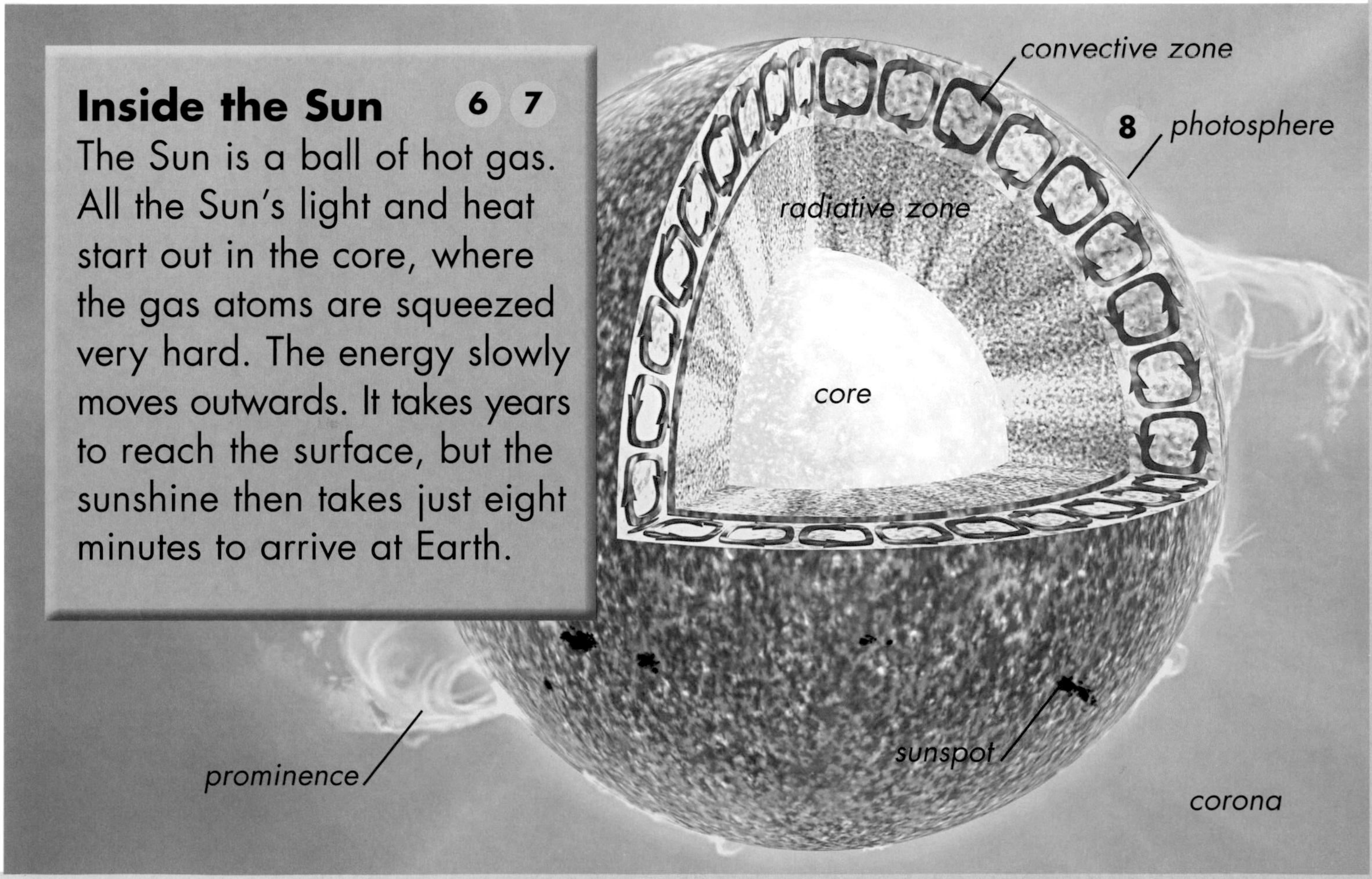

convective zone

8 photosphere

radiative zone

core

prominence

sunspot

corona

Drought

A drought happens when an area runs out of water, normally because it does not rain for a long time. The soil dries out, plants die and animals have nothing to eat.

1 Where can zebras smell water?

2 What do some frogs do when a drought arrives?

3 What happens to soil in a drought?

4 Unjumble STUD VELDIS for winds carrying dust.

5 What do camels store in their humps?

6 How long can a camel go without having a drink?

7 What happens to farm animals during droughts?

8 Name a place that suffers droughts.

Surviving drought   1 2

Nothing can live without water. Large animals walk for days looking for water. Zebras can smell water under the ground and dig it up with their hooves. Other animals, such as frogs, bury themselves in the soil and lie waiting for the rains to return.

Dust devil   3 4

Droughts make the soil so dry that it turns into dust. There are no plant roots to hold the soil together. The dust is blown away by the wind, making swirling dust devils.

Fatty humps 5 6

Camels store fat in their humps and live for months on just dry, salty grass. They can survive for ten days without any food or water at all.

zebra

Difficult times 7 8

In bad droughts, farm animals die of thirst and crops fail, so people have nothing to eat. Africa often suffers droughts. These women are collecting emergency supplies of water.

Clouds

Clouds are tiny droplets of water and crystals of ice that float in the air. The droplets form around specks of dust that are blown in the wind.

1 Name three types of precipitation.

2 What happens when a cloud's water gets too heavy?

3 Re-arrange RRICUS to spell the name of a high cloud.

4 What are fluffy clouds called?

5 What do we call the largest clouds?

6 How tall can a storm cloud be?

7 What two types of cloud form near the ground?

8 Mist is thicker than fog. True or false?

Weather watch   1 2

Rain, hail and snow all start out in clouds. They are all types of precipitation, which falls once the water in the cloud gets too heavy to stay floating in the air.

cirrus

cirrocumulus

Cloud types 3 4
Different types of cloud have different names. High clouds are cirrus. The lowest ones are stratus. A fluffy cloud is a cumulus, while a grey rain cloud is a nimbus or a nimbostratus.

cumulonimbus

altocumulus

Storm clouds 5 6
The largest type of cloud is the cumulonimbus. That is where thunderstorms happen. Storm clouds can be more than ten kilometres high and are sometimes called thunderheads.

cumulus

nimbostratus

stratus

Fog and mist 7 8
Clouds that form near the ground are known as fog and mist. Fog is too thick to see very far. Mist is the name for thinner clouds that are easier to see through.

Rain and flood

Rain is our main supply of freshwater – unsalted water. Rain is needed for crops to grow and for drinking. However, very heavy rain can be dangerous.

1 Where does water move during the the water cycle?

2 How does water get into the air?

3 How does rainwater get back to the sea?

4 What happens if there is too much rain?

5 Unjumble AFSHL ODOFL.

6 What happens at a warm front?

7 What sort of weather is created at cold fronts?

8 Warm fronts produce heavy rain. True or false?

Water cycle

1 2 3

Rain is part of the water cycle that moves water between the sea, the atmosphere (air) and the land. Water evaporates into the air and forms clouds. The clouds drop rain or snow back into the sea or on to land, where the water flows down rivers into the sea.

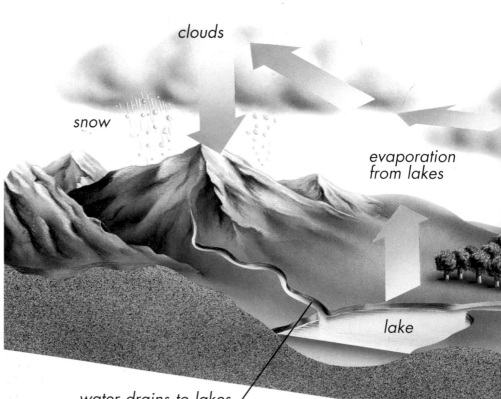

clouds

snow

evaporation from lakes

lake

water drains to lakes or the sea as rivers

Too much rain ④ ⑤

A flood occurs when rain falls faster than it can drain away. It is called a flash flood when this happens suddenly and river levels rise quickly.

At the front ⑥ ⑦ ⑧

Rain happens at fronts. A cold front is the edge of an area of cold air. A warm front is where warmer air rises above colder air. Showers form over cold fronts. Warm fronts create heavy rain.

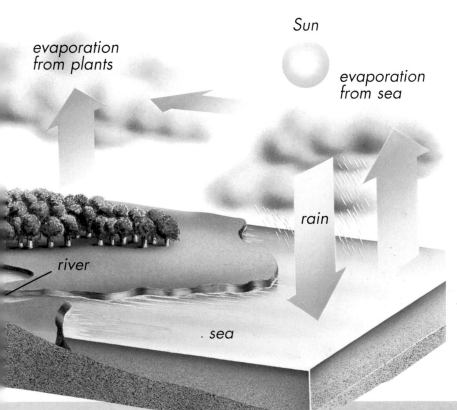

Sun

evaporation from plants

evaporation from sea

rain

river

sea

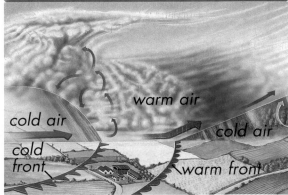

warm air

cold air

cold air

cold front

warm front

Thunder and lightning

Lightning is a huge spark of electricity that is created inside storm clouds. A flash of lightning is formed as the electricity heats up the air. Thunder is the sound of lightning.

1 How does electricity build up inside clouds?

2 Unjumble LINGINGHT TREKIS.

3 Most lightning travels from clouds to the ground. True or false?

4 Lightning is cold. True or false?

5 What damage can lightning cause?

6 How does sound move through air?

7 The sound of thunder is called a snap. True or false?

8 What does lightning do to air?

Spectacular display 1 2 3
Electricity builds up in clouds when the air inside rubs against itself. The electricity stays inside the cloud until the charge becomes large enough to travel through the air. Then a lightning strike runs down from the cloud to the ground.

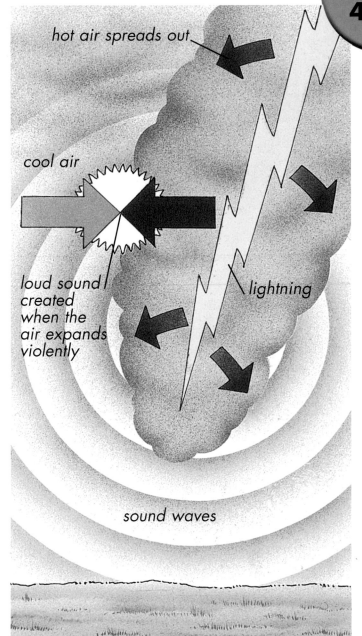

hot air spreads out

cool air

loud sound created when the air expands violently

lightning

sound waves

Destructive power 4 5

Lightning is hotter than the centre of the Earth! It can make trees explode and set forests on fire. Lightning also kills hundreds of people each year.

Thunderclaps 6 7 8

Sound is carried by waves travelling through the air. Thunderclaps are the waves created when the lightning's electricity heats the air. The hot air spreads out in all directions from the lightning. It pushes against the cooler air around it, creating a large sound wave.

Hail and snow

Sometimes the air is too cold for rain. The water in clouds freezes and becomes hail and snow. Snow falls in winter, but hail can occur all year round.

1 What blows rain upwards to form hailstones?

2 Unjumble AIHL to spell a type of frozen raindrop.

3 What shape is a snowflake?

4 When do large snowflakes form?

5 Snowflakes fall quickly. True or false?

6 When does snow build up on the ground?

7 How much more space than rain does snow take up?

8 What machine clears snow away?

How hail forms

1 2

A hailstone is a raindrop that has been blown upwards by a warm wind. The drop freezes as it falls back through colder air. A hailstone may do this several times and build up many layers of ice.

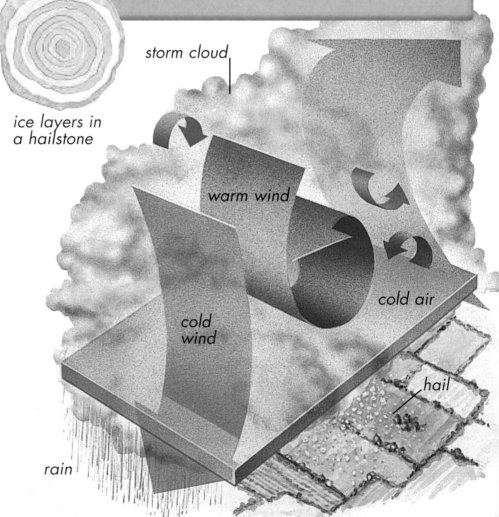

ice layers in a hailstone

storm cloud

warm wind

cold air

cold wind

hail

rain

Ice flakes   3   4   5

Snow is rain that freezes high above the ground in very cold air. The water forms into unique hexagonal (six-sided) flakes. In very wet air, the snowflakes grow into large, beautiful patterns that float slowly to the ground.

Snowed in   6   7   8

If the ground is also very cold, snowflakes build up in thick layers. Snow takes up ten times the space of rain. A heavy fall of snow can cover the ground in snow, metres deep. Snowploughs (right) are used to sweep away the snow from roads.

Wind

Wind is air moving. Air pressure measures how much air is packed together. Wind blows from a high-pressure area to a place with low pressure.

1 How does wind make waves on the ocean?

2 What do waves do when they reach land?

3 Unjumble MMAENOTERE.

4 What do an anemometer's cups do in the wind?

5 Winds blow away from the tropics. True or false?

6 What pushes wind sideways?

7 What parts of the world do westerly winds blow to?

8 What is a windsock for?

Wave after wave   1   2

Ocean waves are formed by strong winds blowing over calm water far out to sea. The waves roll over the surface of the ocean for days before they break, or topple over, on the land.

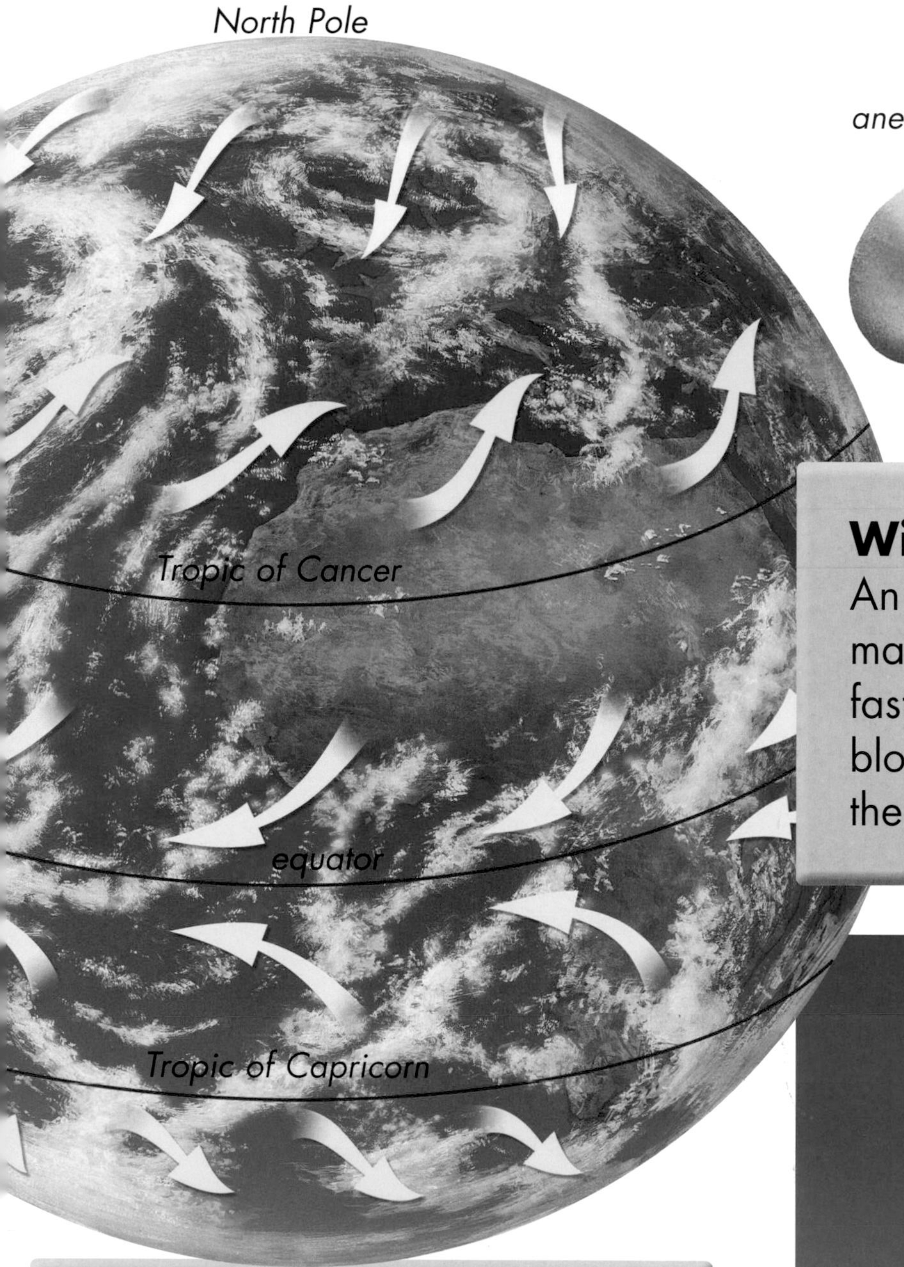

North Pole

Tropic of Cancer

equator

Tropic of Capricorn

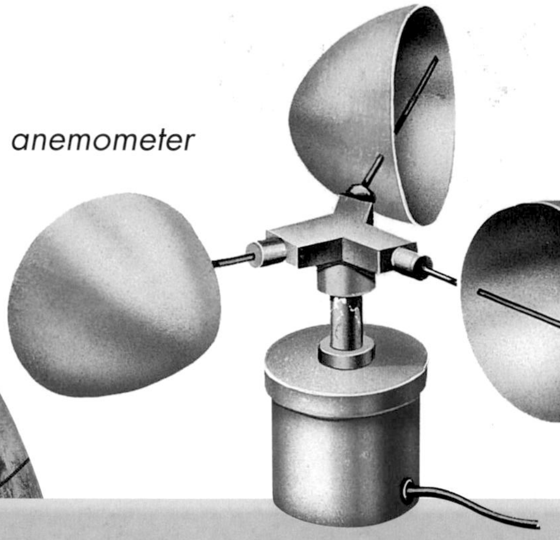

anemometer

Wind speed 3 4

An anemometer is a special machine for measuring how fast the wind is. The wind blows into the cups, making them spin around.

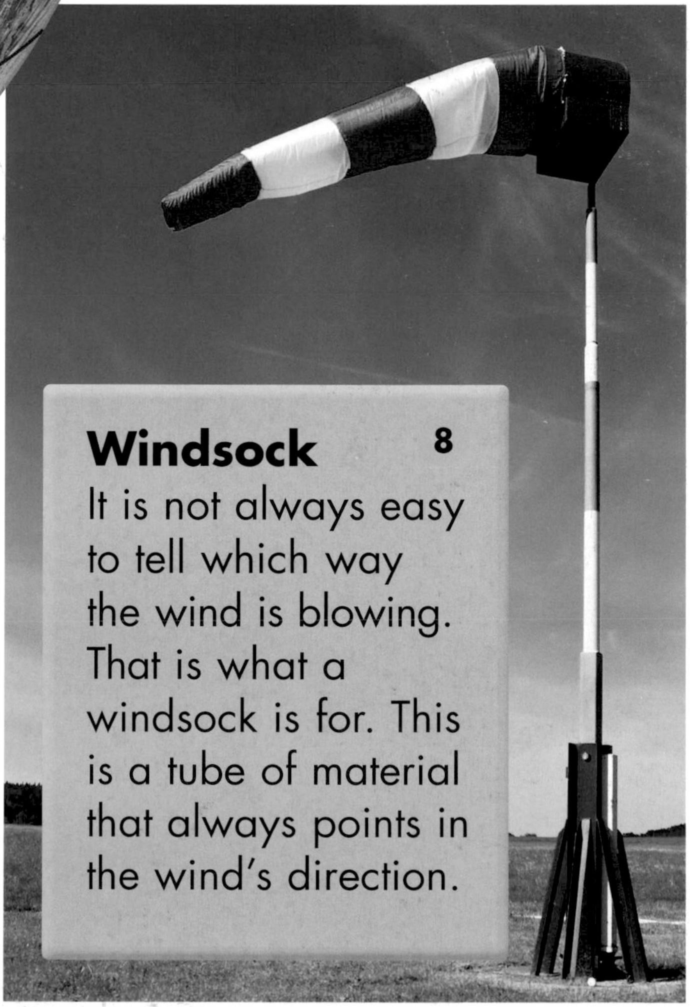

Windsock 8

It is not always easy to tell which way the wind is blowing. That is what a windsock is for. This is a tube of material that always points in the wind's direction.

Wind direction 5 6 7

Ocean winds normally blow in one direction. They head away from the warm tropics, but they do not blow in a straight line. They are pushed sideways by the way Earth turns. Winds heading towards the equator blow from the east. Westerly winds blow towards the Poles.

Hurricanes and cyclones

Tropical cyclones are Earth's biggest storms. They are called hurricanes in the Atlantic Ocean and typhoons in the western Pacific Ocean.

1 Unjumble EUHRRCIAN.

2 Hurricanes form over cold seas. True or false?

3 What is the centre of a hurricane called?

4 What is the air pressure like in the hurricane's eye?

5 How fast are hurricane winds?

6 What do scientists use to watch hurricanes?

7 What is the most dangerous part of a hurricane?

8 What causes a storm surge?

How hurricanes work   1   2   3   4

Hurricanes are formed over warm seas, and are huge clouds of up to 500 kilometres wide. At the centre is the eye, where the air pressure is very low, causing strong winds.

cool air sucked in

eye

wind swirls around eye

updraught

downdraught

strong circulating winds

High wind 5

Hurricane winds blow at more than 119 kilometres per hour. Some have winds that are more than twice as strong. Hurricanes also produce heavy rain.

rings of cloud

Tracking hurricanes 6

Hurricanes are very dangerous. Scientists use satellites to watch them, so they can predict which areas of land they might hit.

Destructive power 7 8

The most dangerous part of the hurricane is the storm surge. This is a wall of seawater several metres high that is blown on to the land by the hurricane's strong winds.

Tornadoes

Tornadoes are also known as whirlwinds and twisters. They are the fastest winds on Earth. The biggest tornadoes occur in the United States.

1 Re-arrange TORVEX to spell a spiral of wind.

2 How fast is a tornado's wind?

3 Do tornadoes form on hot or cold days?

4 What is a waterspout?

5 How are most people killed by tornadoes?

6 Where is the best place to see a tornado?

7 Unjumble NORTDAO LLAEY.

8 How many tornadoes does Tornado Alley have each year?

Swirling menace 1 2 3

Tornadoes are a spiral of wind – known as a vortex. The wind at their centre can swirl around at more than 480 kilometres per hour. Tornadoes form on hot days when storm clouds begin to spin close to the ground.

Waterspout 4

When tornadoes form over the sea they create a waterspout. The wind sucks up seawater, making a column of spray.

Destruction   5

A tornado is very dangerous. Every year dozens of people are killed by objects thrown by the high winds. Occasionally, tornadoes rip through towns and knock down houses.

Tornado Alley   6   7   8

The best place to see a tornado is the Great Plains of North America. This area is nicknamed Tornado Alley. There are 1,000 of the storms there every year.

Seasons

1 When does a tree grow new leaves?

2 What happens to leaves in autumn?

3 Unjumble ECIDDUOUS for a type of tree that has no leaves in winter.

4 What colour do the leaves turn in autumn?

5 Why does Earth have seasons?

6 Where does the northern hemisphere point in winter?

7 The equator has four seasons. True or false?

8 What season does it rain at the equator?

Each year, Earth's temperate zones have four seasons. Every season brings with it a certain type of weather. The season in the northern hemisphere, or top half of the Earth, is always the opposite of the season in the south.

spring   *summer*

Tree changes   1 2 3

In spring a deciduous tree sprouts new leaves. The tree grows fastest during the summer. In autumn its leaves fall off, and the tree stands bare for the cold winter.

Earth orbits the Sun once a year

northern spring

southern autumn

summer in the north

winter in the south

Sun

north points away in northern winter

south tilts towards Sun in southern summer

axis is tilted to one side

northern autumn

southern spring

4

autumn

winter

Tilted planet   5   6

The seasons are produced by the way Earth is tilted to one side. It is summer in the half of the Earth that leans towards the Sun, and it is winter in the half that leans away from the Sun. Spring and autumn happen in between, when neither hemisphere is nearer the Sun than the other.

Wet and dry seasons   7   8

Places near the equator, around the middle of Earth, are hot all year and only have two seasons: the wet season, when it rains a lot, and the dry season with almost no rain.

Spring

In spring, Earth begins to warm up after the cold winter. This is the time of year when plants begin to grow again and when many baby animals are born.

1 Re-arrange NIVEX to spell the name for a female fox.

2 About how many cubs does a fox have each spring?

3 How long do cubs stay in their den?

4 Bluebells grow in fields. True or false?

5 What colour is apple blossom?

6 What do apple blossoms grow into?

7 What type of plant do lambs eat?

8 How long will it be before a lamb is fully grown?

Fox family 1 2 3

A female fox, or vixen, gives birth to four or five cubs every spring. The cubs are born at this time because their mother will be able to find plenty of food for them for the next few months. The cubs spend four weeks in the den before coming out to play in late spring.

Blossom and flowers   4 5 6

Many plants produce flowers and blossoms in spring. Bluebells cover the ground in woodlands. Apple trees produce white blossoms (left), which will have grown into tasty apples by the autumn.

Lambing season   7 8

Spring is a good time for lambs to be born. The grass has started to grow after the cold winter, and the lambs will have enough to eat all summer long. The lambs are fully grown in a year, and some will have babies of their own next spring.

Summer

The warmest season of the year is summer. Summer days are longer than the nights. On midsummer's day, the Sun is up for 16 hours.

1 What are sunflower seeds used for?

2 Sunflowers stay facing one way. True or false?

3 Why is the sea warm in summer?

4 Re-arrange TTELUCE to spell a summer crop.

5 Name a fruit grown in summer.

6 Plants grow slowly in the summer. True or false?

7 Where do swallows spend the winter?

8 When do swallows lay their eggs?

Big heads 1 2

Sunflowers are grown for the oil in the seeds. At sunrise, sunflowers face towards the Sun. The flowers swing west, tracking the Sun through the sky. The flowers move back to the east at night.

At the beach 3

People like to take holidays in summer. They often spend them at the seaside, where the sunny weather makes the sea warm enough to swim in.

Summer crops 4 5 6

In summer, farmers plant crops such as lettuces, cucumbers, strawberries and tomatoes. The plants grow quickly in the long, sunny days and are ready to eat within a few weeks.

Summer visitors 7 8

Some types of birds travel to a new home in summer. Swallows (right) spend the wintertime in warm parts of Africa, but they fly to Europe in summer. The swallows lay their eggs in summer and feed their chicks on flying insects.

Autumn

Autumn is the time of year when wildlife gets ready for winter. Trees drop their leaves and plants produce seeds ready to grow next spring.

1 When are apples ready to eat?

2 What happens during a harvest?

3 Where do brent geese fly in autumn?

4 What is the birds' journey known as?

5 Monarch butterflies go to Canada in autumn. True or false?

6 How many monarch butterflies gather in Mexico?

7 Unjumble PWASN to spell a word for salmon breeding.

8 What happens to salmon after spawning?

Harvest time   1 2

Apples are ready to eat in autumn. They have taken all summer to ripen. Collecting crops is called harvesting. The harvest makes autumn a busy time for farmers.

Migrating geese 3 4

Brent geese spend the summer in the far north. In autumn, they fly south before it gets too cold to find insects to eat. This journey is called a migration.

brent geese

Butterflies 5 6

In autumn, a billion monarch butterflies from all over North America fly south to Mexico, where they crowd into a few forests until the winter is over.

Salmon 7 8

In autumn, salmon swim out of the sea and head up rivers to breed, or spawn. The salmon must swim against the current and jump up waterfalls. After they spawn, the fish die.

Winter

In winter, the nights are longer than the days. As a result, the weather is cold. It is too dark and cold for plants to grow, and animals find it hard to find food.

1 What colour is an Arctic fox?

2 How can being white help an animal in winter?

3 Unjumble SYNWO WLO to name a type of bird that lives in the Arctic.

4 At what temperature does water freeze?

5 Where do wood frogs hibernate?

6 What do chipmunks snack on in winter?

7 For how long does a dormouse sleep?

8 Where do badgers live?

Surviving winter 2
Animals that live in places with long, cold winters often have white feathers or fur. This colouring camouflages the animals, making it hard for predators to spot them in the snow.

ptarmigan

1 *Arctic fox*

3 *snowy owl*

Snowfall ⁴

The temperature in winter can drop below 0°C, and water may freeze into ice. Often, there is snow instead of rain, and the snow can stay covering the ground for weeks.

Arctic hare

Hibernation ⁵ ⁶ ⁷ ⁸

Many animals hibernate, or go into a deep sleep for the winter.
A Wood frogs burrow into riverbanks and can survive being frozen solid.
B Chipmunks snack on a store of seeds throughout the winter.
C A dormouse sleeps for seven months without waking.
D Badgers do not hibernate but will stay in their warm sett on the very coldest nights.

Global warming

Our planet is kept warm by the air. Without this layer of gases, Earth would be a frozen world with no running water. The air warms us through the greenhouse effect, but people may now be making Earth too hot.

1. What gas is: BARCON OXIDIED?

2. How does carbon dioxide (CO_2) make the world warmer?

3. How do animals put CO_2 into the air?

4. What do plants make from CO_2?

5. Name a type of fuel that produces CO_2.

6. Levels of CO_2 in the air have gone up. True or false?

7. Why do people cut down forests?

8. What happens to soil after forests are cut down?

Greenhouse effect   1   2

The air contains a tiny amount of carbon dioxide gas (CO_2). Carbon dioxide lets the energy from the Sun shine on to Earth's surface, but it also stops heat from escaping back into space. As a result, Earth stays warm, as if it was wrapped in a blanket.

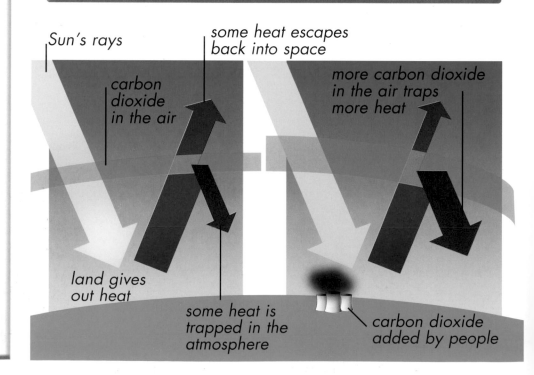

Sun's rays

some heat escapes back into space

carbon dioxide in the air

more carbon dioxide in the air traps more heat

land gives out heat

some heat is trapped in the atmosphere

carbon dioxide added by people

Gas from life 3 4

Carbon dioxide is added to the air naturally when animals breathe out. It is the waste gas created when living things burn up food. Plants release the gas, too. They also take in carbon dioxide from the air and use it to make sugar.

Gas pollution 5 6

Burning fuels such as petrol produces carbon dioxide. Over the last 200 years people have burned so much fuel that there is now a lot more carbon dioxide in the air. The greenhouse effect means this extra gas is making Earth hotter.

forest trees are burned

Losing forests 7

Cutting down forests to make way for farms makes global warming worse. The trees are burned and that adds carbon dioxide to the air. The best way to take the gas out of the air again is to let a forest grow back.

 without trees, soil washes away

Climate change

People are making the world hotter. We are doing this by burning fuels. This adds carbon dioxide to the air, which in turn traps heat in the atmosphere. This heat is changing the climate.

1 What will happen as the oceans get warmer?

2 Where did the government of the Maldives meet?

3 Ice at the North Pole is melting. True or false?

4 What ice-loving animal is ROPLA RBEA?

5 How is climate change making forests drier?

6 What natural event can start a fire?

7 Where do corals grow?

8 When do corals go white?

Underwater summit

1 2

As the world's oceans get warmer, sea levels will go up. It could rise by several metres in the next few hundred years, meaning that many islands will be covered by the sea. The government of the Maldives had a meeting underwater to highlight the problem facing their islands.

Melting ice sheet 3 4

Global warming created by humans is melting the ice that covers the sea at the North Pole. Polar bears live on the ice and have fewer places to hunt.

Forest fire 5 6

Climate change may be causing more forest fires. Forests get less rain and become very dry. Lightning strikes set the trees on fire, which take many days to put out.

Dying coral 7 8

Coral grows in warm, shallow seas. Corals are animals but they have tiny coloured plants living inside. Climate change is making the water so warm that the plants die. This makes the coral go white.

WEATHER AND CLIMATE
Record breakers

1. The fastest wind ever recorded was 512 kilometres per hour inside a tornado near Oklahoma City, USA in 1999.

2. The highest wave ever seen was 27 metres, caused by a storm in the Atlantic Ocean in 2005.

3. The largest outbreak of tornadoes happened in April 1973, when 148 tornadoes formed in the United States in just 24 hours.

4. The world's sunniest place is Yuma, Arizona, USA. On average, it is sunny for 4,127 hours every year.

5. The driest place on Earth is the Atacama Desert in Peru – it did not rain at all between 1571 and 1971!

6. The rainiest place on Earth is Waialeale, Hawaii, where it rains on 335 days of every year.

7. The largest hailstone ever seen was 17.8 centimetres wide.

8. The largest hurricane was Typhoon Tip, which formed in the Pacific Ocean in 1979. It was 1,100 kilometres across.

9. The highest clouds in Earth's atmosphere form at a height of 85 kilometres.

10. The fastest temperature rise ever recorded was 56°C in 24 hours in 1972, in Loma, Montana, USA.

Chapter three
PROTECTING NATURE

Life on Earth

As far as we know, Earth is the only planet with life. Life appeared about four billion years ago. Today, there are millions of types of living things.

1 The largest animal is the green whale. True or false?

2 What is heavier, a blue whale or 10 elephants?

3 What are the smallest living things?

4 How many bacteria fit on a full stop?

5 Where does the goliath beetle live?

6 What bug does MILPDILEE spell?

7 What is the fastest animal on Earth?

8 Name the fastest fish in the sea.

Giant beasts **1 2**

The blue whale is the largest animal that ever lived. It grows to 30 metres and weighs as much as 30 elephants!

Too small to see ③ ④

About half of all life is invisible without a microscope. Bacteria are the smallest living things. Several thousands would fit on a full stop.

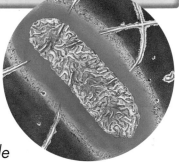

goliath beetle

Giant bugs ⑤ ⑥

The heaviest insect is the goliath beetle from Africa. It weighs 100 grams but can still fly. The largest millipedes also come from Africa. They reach 35 cm long. Ants form the largest societies on Earth. Some colonies contain billions of insects.

millipede

rhinoceros beetle

Fastest animals ⑦ ⑧

The fastest-moving animal is the peregrine falcon, which dives towards the ground at 320 kilometres per hour. The fastest sea creature is the sailfish, which can swim at 110 kilometres per hour.

peregrine falcon

Evolution

Living things change. This is called evolution, and it helps life survive as conditions change. Most animals from the past have become extinct, or died out.

1 What does *Eohippus* mean?

2 How many toes did *Eohippus* have?

3 A horse's hoof is used for swimming. True or false?

4 When did the last dinosaurs die out?

5 How do we know about dinosaurs?

6 Who explained how evolution works?

7 Where was Charles Darwin from?

8 Why are animals all slightly different from each other?

Eohippus

Miohippus

Merychippus

Pliohippus

Horse

Evolution of the horse ① ② ③

Horses, donkeys and zebras all evolved from one ancestor that lived 60 million years ago. The animal was called *Eohippus*, which means 'dawn horse'. It was only 40 centimetres tall and had four toes. *Eohippus* lived in the forest, but it slowly evolved to live on open grasslands. Each new type grew taller, and their toes evolved into a single long hoof that was better for running.

Dinosaurs   **4** **5**

Millions of years ago, the largest animals on land were dinosaurs. The last of the dinosaurs died out 65 million years ago. All we know about them comes from fossils.

Coelophysis *fossil*

Charles Darwin   **6** **7** **8**

Evolution was first explained by the English scientist Charles Darwin. He saw how animals, such as different types of finch, looked similar but had small variations. Darwin realised that evolution had created these variations so each finch was suited to life in different places.

finch

Water for life

Three-quarters of the human body is made of water. Life could not exist without it. The people of the world use five trillion litres of water ever year.

1 Why is extra water put on some crops?

2 Rice fields are called paddies. True or false?

3 Re-arrange RSRVOREEI for a place where we store water.

4 How are reservoirs made?

5 Where do canals and pipes take water to?

6 Where can you find clean water?

7 Where does a bottle tree grow?

8 Where does a bottle tree store its water?

Water for food ①②

Nearly three-quarters of the water we use goes on to farmland. Crops often need extra water to grow properly. Rice grows in flooded fields called paddies.

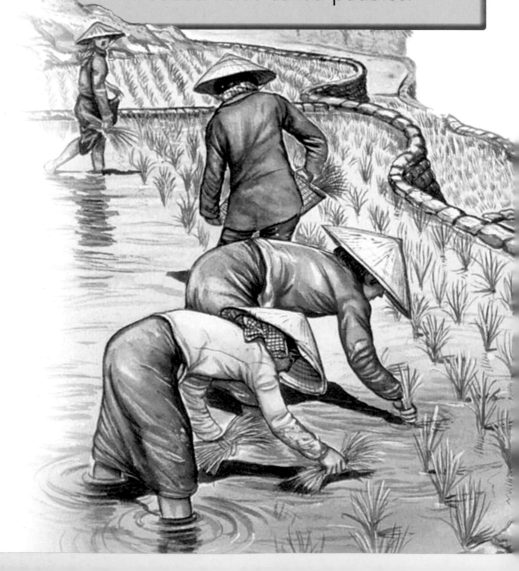

Reservoirs ③④⑤

We store our water in man-made lakes, or reservoirs. Most reservoirs form behind a dam – a wall that is built across a river. Canals and pipes take the water from the reservoir to cities and farms.

Play pump ⑥

People need clean water. A good place to get it is from under the ground. The water from this tap is pumped out of the ground when children play on the roundabout.

Bottle tree ⑦⑧

The Australian baobab tree grows in dry places and stores water inside a thick, swollen trunk. Aboriginal Australians call it the bottle tree. They dig into the trunk to collect water. Similar baobab trees grow in Africa.

Harming the planet

Human beings have learnt to change the environment to make it suit their needs. However, by doing so they have caused many problems.

1 Where does most of our rubbish go?

2 What happens once a landfill site is full?

3 Why are some forests getting smaller?

4 Re-arrange LLOPUTION to spell dangerous chemicals.

5 Where does pollution go?

6 Where does oil come from?

7 Spilt oil is called a slick. True or false?

8 How do people save animals hurt by oil slicks?

Landfill **1** **2**

Every person in Europe throws away 500 kilograms of rubbish every year. It ends up in a giant hole called a landfill site. When it is full, the landfill site will be covered in soil.

Cutting logs ③

We use wood for many things, and it all comes from a forest. In some parts of the world, people are cutting down the forest trees faster than they can grow back. The forests are shrinking fast.

Pollution ④ ⑤

Dangerous chemicals, or pollution, are produced by factories and released into the air and water. Pollution can kill plants and animals.

Oil spills ⑥ ⑦ ⑧

Petroleum is thick oil found under the ground. Ships take it around the world. Sometimes these ships spill oil, covering coasts in a slick. The oil will kill animals unless it is cleaned off.

Clean energy

Burning fuels to make the energy we need is damaging our planet. People are looking for clean ways of making electricity without using fuels.

1 How do turbines catch the wind?

2 What turns inside a wind turbine?

3 What part of a generator does GNETMA spell?

4 Wave power helps generate energy. True or false?

5 Unjumble GETHMALERO.

6 Where does a geothermal power plant get its heat?

7 Semiconductors are used in solar panels. True or false?

8 What happens when light shines on a solar panel?

Wind turbines ① ② ③

Turbines are high-tech windmills. The long blades are shaped to catch the wind, so the turbine spins around. The spinning movement turns a generator inside. This is a machine that uses magnets to make electricity.

electricity generator

Wave power station 4

Wave machines float on the sea and produce electricity from the waves. The waves make each section rock up and down, and that movement powers generators inside.

Hot water 5 6

Geothermal power uses underground volcanic heat to boil water. This creates steam that is used to power generators.

Solar panels 7 8

We catch the energy in sunlight using solar panels. The panels contain semi-conductors, which convert the energy from sunlight directly into electricity.

Endangered animals

Many animals are very rare. One day soon they may become extinct – gone for ever. These endangered animals need our help to survive.

1 Where do rhinoceroses live?

2 Why were rhinoceroses hunted?

3 How many mountain gorillas live in the wild?

4 What do mountain gorillas eat?

5 What is the largest cat in the world?

6 Unjumble SIAA to spell where tigers live.

7 Where do turtles lay their eggs?

8 What are many turtle beaches used for by people?

Killed for their horn ❶❷

Rhinoceroses live in Africa and Asia. For years they were killed for their horns, which people thought had special power. Today, rhinos are safer, but there are very few left.

Mountain gorilla ③ ④

There are only about 700 mountain gorillas left in the wild. They are the largest primates in the world and weigh twice as much as an adult human. They eat leaves, flowers and roots but their forest home is shrinking as people turn the land into farms.

Biggest cat ⑤ ⑥

The tiger is the world's largest cat, and it is also one of the rarest. Tigers lives all over eastern Asia, but there are few places left where they can hunt.

Sea turtles ⑦ ⑧

Female turtles lay their eggs on sandy beaches, but they are frightened off by people. Many turtle beaches are used as holiday resorts, and fewer turtles lay eggs there each year.

Recycling

One way to reduce rubbish is to recycle. Glass, paper and metal do not need to be thrown away. We can make them into new things.

1 Why is it good to sort out your rubbish?

2 Unjumble COSOTPM.

3 What can you compost at home?

4 What happens at a recycling plant?

5 What pulls metals out of mixed-up rubbish?

6 Paper is separated from rubbish with a fan. True or false?

7 What can paper be made into?

8 Name something that can be made from plastic bottles.

Sorting out waste ❶
How many bins have you got in your house? Many people have a bin for each type of rubbish. That makes it much easier to collect things for recycling.

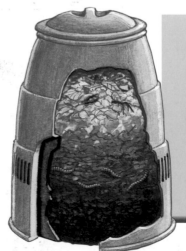

Composting ❷ ❸
Food can be turned into compost – rich soil used for growing plants. Fruit and vegetables can even be composted at home.

Recycling plant

4

Rubbish cannot be recycled if it is all mixed together. It needs to be sorted out into each type of material. A recycling plant uses many clever ways to divide up the rubbish automatically.

mixture of rubbish comes in here

5

metals pulled on to conveyor belt by magnets

paper blown out of rubbish by a fan

fan

6

Reuses

7 **8**

Recycled metal is melted down and used to make new metal objects. Old paper is pulped and made into cardboard. Glass can be made into new bottles or it is crushed up and used as gravel in road building. Plastic bottles are made into anything from chairs to warm jackets.

heavy bottles fall through the gaps

glass sorted into colours

wet paper falls down here

leftovers sent to a landfill site

Helping save the planet

People have damaged the natural world, and it is up to us to fix the problems we have caused. There are many ways to look after the planet.

1 What could help save our planet?

2 What do cleaner cars run on?

3 What is conservation?

4 Unjumble DAPNA for a giant, rare animal.

5 Name a charity that works to save rare animals.

6 World leaders and scientists meet to fix which problem?

7 What could you do to help save the planet?

8 Is it better to get food grown near home or far away?

How can industry help? ① ②

New technology could save the planet. For example, cars produce a lot of pollution. Car-makers are working to make cleaner cars that run on electricity or hydrogen fuel. Modern factories use less energy and water and give out less pollution. People are also trying to make products that can be recycled rather than just thrown away.

Charities ③ ④ ⑤

Protecting rare animals and plants, such as giant pandas, is called conservation. People give money to charities, such as the World Wildlife Fund (WWF) and the International Union for Conservation of Nature, which work hard to save endangered animals.

Agreements ⑥

Climate change is a big problem for the planet. World leaders and top scientists meet regularly to try to agree ways to proceed. But they find it hard to agree what they need to do.

What about you? ⑦ ⑧

Everyone has to look after nature. What can you do? Perhaps you could walk or cycle to school and not use the car. Or you could buy food that is grown locally, because transporting it long distances creates lots of pollution.

PROTECTING NATURE
Record breakers

1. The most endangered type of animal are amphibians. A third of all frogs and newts are in danger of extinction.

2. The oldest fossils are piles of bacteria called stromatolites, dating back 3.45 billion years!

3. The rarest mammal is the Vancouver Island marmot, from Canada. There are only about 30 living wild.

4. The largest geothermal power plant is at Geysers, California, USA. It provides power for 750,000 homes.

5. The largest pile of rubbish is the Great Pacific Ocean Garbage Patch, with 100 million tonnes of plastic.

6. The largest oil spill happened when two ships collided near Trinidad in 1979. About 287,000 tonnes were spilt.

7. The world's largest reservoir is Lake Kariba on the Zambezi River, Africa. It contains enough water to fill 57 million Olympic swimming pools.

8. The strongest animal is the rhinoceros beetle. It can carry 850 times its own weight!

9. The fastest electric car is the Buckeye Bullet, which has a top speed of 517 kilometres per hour.

10. The most efficient vehicle ever invented is the bicycle.

ANSWERS

Did you get it right? Now it is time to check your answers and see how well you have done! Good luck...

Habitats

Rainforests

1 Where do ocelots hunt in the rainforest?

Answer: In the tree branches

2 Unjumble GARAJU to spell the name of a big jungle cat.

Answer: JAGUAR

3 What is the loudest animal in the rainforest?

Answer: A howler monkey

4 For how long can a macaw live?

Answer: 75 years

5 When do army ants make camp?

Answer: At night

6 Who guards an army ant queen?

Answer: Soldier ants

7 In what part of the world do poison dart frogs live?

Answer: Central and South America

8 Is it safe for other animals to eat a poison dart frog?

Answer: No, because it is poisonous

Temperate forests

1 What colour is the forest's main hunter?

Answer: Red (red fox)

2 What does a jay do in autumn?

Answer: Buries nuts

3 Where does a badger live?

Answer: Underground

4 Re-arrange MELAP to spell the name of a forest tree.

Answer: MAPLE

5 Deciduous trees keep their leaves all year around. True or false?

Answer: False

6 What colour do the leaves change to in autumn?

Answer: Brown

7 Why do leaves go brown before they fall off?

Answer: The leaves stop producing the green pigment chlorophyll

8 Where do koala bears live?

Answer: Australia

Taiga forests

1 Most taiga forest trees are evergreen. True or false?

Answer: True

2 What shape are the leaves of trees in taiga forests?

Answer: Needle-shaped

3 Name four types of food eaten by brown bears.

Answer: Roots, fungi, berries and fish

4 What colour is a squirrel living in taiga forests?

Answer: Red

5 How does a woodpecker make a hole in bark?

Answer: With its sharp beak

6 What colour is a timber wolf?

Answer: Grey

7 Unjumble YNXL to name a wild cat.

Answer: LYNX

8 Why do lynx need large paws?

Answer: To walk on the snow

Deserts

1 Unjumble ASIOS to name a desert area with a water supply.

Answer: OASIS

2 Where does the water in an oasis come from?

Answer: Underground rivers

3 Where is the Sahara Desert?

Answer: In Africa

4 A mountain desert is always hot. True or false?

Answer: False

5 What does the wind do to the rocks in a desert?

Answer: It wears them away

6 Where does a cactus keep water?

Answer: In its wide stem

7 Why does a fennec fox hunt at night?

Answer: Because it is cooler

8 What type of animal is a sidewinder?

Answer: A snake

Tundra

1 The tundra is hot all year round. True or false?

Answer: False

2 What kind of plants grow on the tundra?

Answer: Small plants

3 Unjumble NSOYW WOL.

Answer: SNOWY OWL

4 What do many tundra birds feed their chicks?

Answer: Insects

5 At what time of year do reindeer live on the tundra?

Answer: In summer

6 What do reindeer do in the winter?

Answer: Shelter in the forest

7 Where is most of the world's tundra?

Answer: Near the North Pole

8 What grows on mountain tundra?

Answer: Plants and grasses

Mountains

1 What is the top of a mountain called?

Answer: The summit

2 Where is Mount Everest?

Answer: In the Himalayas in Asia

3 What is a river of ice on a mountain called?

Answer: A glacier

4 What do glaciers do to rocks?

Answer: They grind them away

5 Mountain plants are always very big. True or false?

Answer: False

6 Re-arrange BSOWNELL to spell a type of mountain flower.

Answer: SNOWBELL

7 Where do ibex goats live?

Answer: In the mountains of Africa, Europe and Asia

8 Why do ibex grow thick fur?

Answer: To keep warm

Volcanoes

1 Earth's surface is moving. True or false?

Answer: True

2 Where do most volcanoes form?

Answer: Where plates meet or split

3 Re-arrange LATOL to spell a type of coral island.

Answer: ATOLL

4 In what type of seas do atolls form?

Answer: Warm seas

5 What is hot, liquid rock underground called?

Answer: Magma

6 At what point does magma become lava?

Answer: When it spurts out of a volcano

7 What shape is a common volcano crater?

Answer: A cone

8 What happens when lava cools?

Answer: It becomes rock

Swamps and marshes

1 Why are most plants grow unable to in a swamp or marsh?

Answer: The soil is too wet

2 Where do swamp cypress trees grow?

Answer: In water

3 Where can you see Spanish moss?

Answer: Hanging from branches

4 Re-arrange GATIALLRO to make a type of swamp animal.

Answer: ALLIGATOR

5 Where does a mangrove forest grow?

Answer: In a swamp beside the sea

6 Mangrove tree roots stick out of the soil. True or false?

Answer: True

7 Where do gallinules walk?

Answer: On lily pads

8 What do wetland birds eat?

Answer: Fish, insects and shellfish

Ponds and lakes

1 What do great diving beatles eat?

Answer: Baby insects

2 What is the name for a baby dragonfly?

Answer: A naiad

3 Re-arrange NERMOOH to spell a lake bird.

Answer: MOORHEN

4 What do beavers use to build a dam?

Answer: Logs

5 What does a beaver eat?

Answer: Plants and bark

6 What do tadpoles grow before they become frogs?

Answer: They grow legs

7 Name a type of lake fish.

Answer: A perch, carp or pike

8 Most perch have red fins. True or false?

Answer: True

Rivers

1 Where do capybaras live?

Answer: South America

2 How long is the world's largest rodent?

Answer: One metre long

3 What is a river's source?

Answer: The place where it starts

4 Where would you find an estuary?

Answer: Where a river meets the sea

5 Crocodiles and caimans are frightened of water. True or false?

Answer: False

6 What is an anaconda?

Answer: A snake

7 Do electric eels live in rivers?

Answer: Yes

8 Re-arrange HANAPRI to spell a type of river fish.

Answer: PIRANHA

Rock pools

1 Limpets are not related to snails. True or false?

Answer: False

2 How do scallops move around?

Answer: By squirting jets of water

3 Unjumble the word LLEJYSHFI to spell the name of a stinging animal.

Answer: JELLYFISH

4 What stops crabs from drying out in the air?

Answer: A hard shell

5 What are a crab's gills for?

Answer: Breathing in water and on land

6 Crabs have four legs. True or false?

Answer: False, they have eight

7 How many pincers does a crab have?

Answer: Two

8 Where do most rock pool animals live?

Answer: In pools near to the sea

Coral reefs

1 How do some reef fish eat corals?

Answer: By scraping them from rocks

2 What type of eel lives in coral reefs?

Answer: Moray eel

3 Do sharks ever visit coral reefs?

Answer: Yes

4 What does a sea turtle eat?

Answer: Shellfish

5 There is a type of turtle called an eaglebeak. True or false?

Answer: False, it is a hawksbill

6 Corals are a type of animal. True or false?

Answer: True

7 Unjumble POPYL to spell another word for coral.

Answer: POLYP

8 What lives inside some coral polyps?

Answer: Tiny plants called algae

Deep sea

1 How do some deep-sea animals make their own light?

Answer: With chemicals in their skin

2 Name one reason for making light in the deep sea.

Answer: To trick prey, scare attackers or attract a mate

3 Jellyfish bodies are hard. True or false?

Answer: False

4 How does a jellyfish trap prey?

Answer: With its tentacles

5 What do jellyfish stingers fire?

Answer: Poison

6 Unjumble QDUIS to spell a deep-sea giant.

Answer: SQUID

7 Is a giant squid as long as a bus or a train?

Answer: A bus

8 How many people have seen a giant squid alive?

Answer: None

The Poles

1 What is the name for the area around the North Pole?

Answer: The Arctic

2 What covers most of the Arctic?

Answer: An ocean

3 Name an animal that lives on the Arctic ice.

Answer: A seal, walrus or polar bear

4 Unjumble PLARO EARB.

Answer: POLAR BEAR

5 Where is Antarctica?

Answer: Around the South Pole

6 How do emperor penguins stay warm in winter?

Answer: They huddle together

7 How wide are albatross wings?

Answer: Three metres across

8 What does an albatross use its long wings for?

Answer: Gliding

Weather and climate

Sunshine

1 Sunshine warms Earth. True or false?

Answer: True

2 What do plants use sunshine for?

Answer: To make their food

3 How often does the Sun rise and set?

Answer: Once each day

4 Unjumble SXIA.

Answer: AXIS

5 Are the Poles warmer than the equator?

Answer: No, they are colder

6 What is the Sun made of?

Answer: Hot gas

7 How long does it take for sunshine to reach Earth?

Answer: Eight minutes

8 The surface of the Sun is called the photosphere. True or false?

Answer: True

Drought

1 Where can zebras smell water?

Answer: Under the ground

2 What do some frogs do when a drought arrives?

Answer: They bury themselves

3 What happens to soil in a drought?

Answer: It turns to dust

4 Unjumble STUD VELDIS for winds carrying dust.

Answer: DUST DEVILS

5 What do camels store in their humps?

Answer: Fat

6 How long can a camel go without having a drink?

Answer: Ten days

7 What happens to farm animals during droughts?

Answer: They die of thirst

8 Name a place that suffers droughts.

Answer: Africa

Clouds

1 Name three types of precipitation.

Answer: Rain, hail and snow

2 What happens when a cloud's water gets too heavy?

Answer: It rains

3 Re-arrange RRICUS to spell the name of a high cloud.

Answer: CIRRUS

4 What are fluffy clouds called?

Answer: Cumulus

5 What do we call the largest clouds?

Answer: Cumulonimbus

6 How tall can a storm cloud be?

Answer: Ten kilometres

7 What two types of cloud form near the ground?

Answer: Fog and mist

8 Mist is thicker than fog. True or false?

Answer: False

Rain and flood

1 Where does water move during the the water cycle?

Answer: Between the sea, air and land

2 How does water get into the air?

Answer: It evaporates

3 How does rainwater get back to the sea?

Answer: It flows down rivers

4 What happens if there is too much rain?

Answer: There is a flood

5 Unjumble AFSHL ODOFL.

Answer: FLASH FLOOD

6 What happens at a warm front?

Answer: Warm air rises above cold air

7 What sort of weather is created at cold fronts?

Answer: Showers

8 Warm fronts produce heavy rain. True or false?

Answer: True

Thunder and lightning

1 How does electricity build up inside clouds?

Answer: The air rubs against itself

2 Unjumble LINGINGHT TREKIS.

Answer: LIGHTNING STRIKE

3 Most lightning travels from clouds to the ground. True or false?

Answer: True

4 Lightning is cold. True or false?

Answer: False

5 What damage can lightning cause?

Answer: Trees explode and forests catch fire

6 How does sound move through air?

Answer: As a wave

7 The sound of thunder is a snap. True or false?

Answer: False, it is a clap

8 What does lightning do to air?

Answer: It heats it up

Hail and snow

1 What blows rain upwards to form hailstones?

Answer: A warm wind

2 Unjumble AIHL to spell a type of frozen raindrop.

Answer: HAIL

3 What shape is a snowflake?

Answer: A hexagon

4 When do large snowflakes form?

Answer: When the air is very wet

5 Snowflakes fall quickly. True or false?

Answer: False, they drift down slowly

6 When does snow build up on the ground?

Answer: When the ground is very cold

7 How much more space than rain does snow take up?

Answer: Ten times more space

8 What machine clears snow away?

Answer: A snowplough

Wind

1 How does wind make waves on the ocean?

Answer: It blows over calm water

2 What do waves do when they reach land?

Answer: They break

3 Unjumble MMAENOTERE.

Answer: ANEMOMETER

4 What do an anemometer's cups do in the wind?

Answer: They spin around

5 Winds blow away from the tropics. True or false?

Answer: True

6 What pushes wind sideways?

Answer: The spin of Earth

7 What parts of the world do westerly winds blow to?

Answer: The Poles

8 What is a windsock for?

Answer: For showing the wind direction

Hurricanes and cyclones

1 Unjumble EUHRRCIAN.

Answer: HURRICANE

2 Hurricanes form over cold seas. True or false?

Answer: False

3 What is the centre of a hurricane called?

Answer: The eye

4 What is the air pressure like in the hurricane's eye?

Answer: It is very low

5 How fast are hurricane winds?

Answer: More than 119 km/h

6 What do scientists use to watch hurricanes?

Answer: Satellites

7 What is the most dangerous part of a hurricane?

Answer: The storm surge

8 What causes a storm surge?

Answer: Strong winds pushing water

Tornadoes

1 Re-arrange TORVEX to spell a spiral of wind.

Answer: VORTEX

2 How fast is a tornado's wind?

Answer: More than 480 km/h

3 Do tornadoes form on hot or cold days?

Answer: Hot days

4 What is a waterspout?

Answer: A tornado out to sea

5 How are most people killed by tornadoes?

Answer: By objects blown by the wind

6 Where is the best place to see a tornado?

Answer: Great Plains of North America

7 Unjumble NORTDAO LLAEY.

Answer: TORNADO ALLEY

8 How many tornadoes does Tornado Alley have each year?

Answer: 1,000

Seasons

1 When does a tree grow new leaves?

Answer: In spring

2 What happens to leaves in autumn?

Answer: They fall off

3 Unjumble ECIDDUOUS for a type of tree that has no leaves in winter.

Answer: DECIDUOUS

4 What colour do the leaves turn in autumn?

Answer: Golden brown

5 Why does Earth have seasons?

Answer: Because the Earth is tilted

6 Where does the northern hemisphere point in winter?

Answer: Away from the Sun

7 The equator has four seasons. True or false?

Answer: False, it has only two

8 What season does it rain at the equator?

Answer: In the wet season

Spring

1 Re-arrange NIVEX to spell the name for a female fox.

Answer: VIXEN

2 About how many cubs does a fox have each spring?

Answer: Four or five

3 How long do cubs stay in their den?

Answer: For four weeks

4 Bluebells grow in fields. True or false?

Answer: False, they grow in woods

5 What colour is apple blossom?

Answer: White

6 What do apple blossoms grow into?

Answer: Apple fruits

7 What type of plant do lambs eat?

Answer: Grass

8 How long will it be before a lamb is fully grown?

Answer: One year

Summer

1 What are sunflower seeds used for?

Answer: Their oil

2 Sunflowers stay facing one way. True or false?

Answer: False, they follow the Sun

3 Why is the sea warm in summer?

Answer: Because of the sunny weather

4 Re-arrange TTELUCE to spell a summer crop.

Answer: LETTUCE

5 Name a fruit grown in summer.

Answer: Strawberries or tomatoes

6 Plants grow slowly in the summer. True or false?

Answer: False, they grow quickly

7 Where do swallows spend the winter?

Answer: In Africa

8 When do swallows lay their eggs?

Answer: In summer

Autumn

1 When are apples ready to eat?

Answer: In autumn

2 What happens during a harvest?

Answer: Crops are collected

3 Where do brent geese fly in autumn?

Answer: South

4 What is the birds' journey known as?

Answer: A migration

5 Monarch butterflies go to Canada in autumn. True or false?

Answer: False, they head to Mexico

6 How many monarch butterflies gather in Mexico?

Answer: A billion

7 Unjumble PWASN to spell a word for salmon breeding.

Answer: SPAWN

8 What happens to salmon after spawning?

Answer: They die

Winter

1 What colour is an Arctic fox?

Answer: White

2 How can being white help an animal in winter?

Answer: To camouflage the animal

3 Unjumble SYNWO WLO to name a type of bird that lives in the Arctic.

Answer: SNOWY OWL

4 At what temperature does water freeze?

Answer: 0°C

5 Where do wood frogs hibernate?

Answer: In burrows in riverbanks

6 What do chipmunks snack on in winter?

Answer: A store of seeds

7 For how long does a dormouse sleep?

Answer: Seven months

8 Where do badgers live?

Answer: In a sett

Global warming

1 What gas is: BARCON OXIDIED?

Answer: CARBON DIOXIDE

2 How does carbon dioxide (CO_2) make the world warmer?

Answer: It traps heat in the air

3 How do animals put CO_2 into the air?

Answer: By breathing out

4 What do plants make from CO_2?

Answer: Sugar

5 Name a type of fuel that produces CO_2.

Answer: Petrol

6 Levels of CO_2 in the air have gone up. True or false?

Answer: True

7 Why do people cut down forests?

Answer: To make space for farms

8 What happens to soil after forests are cut down?

Answer: It is washed away

Climate change

1 What will happen as the oceans get warmer?

Answer: The sea level will rise

2 Where did the government of the Maldives meet?

Answer: Underwater

3 Ice at the North Pole is melting. True or false?

Answer: True

4 What ice-loving animal is ROPLA RBEA?

Answer: POLAR BEAR

5 How is climate change making forests drier?

Answer: It rains less on the forest

6 What natural event can start a fire?

Answer: Lightning

7 Where do corals grow?

Answer: In warm, shallow water

8 When do corals go white?

Answer: When the water gets too warm

Protecting nature

Life on Earth

1 The largest animal is the green whale. True or false?

Answer: False, it is the blue whale

2 What is heavier, a blue whale or 10 elephants?

Answer: Blue whale

3 What are the smallest living things?

Answer: Bacteria

4 How many bacteria fit on a full stop?

Answer: Several thousand

5 Where does the goliath beetle live?

Answer: Africa

6 What bug does MILPDILEE spell?

Answer: MILLIPEDE

7 What is the fastest animal on Earth?

Answer: Peregrine falcon

8 Name the fastest fish in the sea.

Answer: Sailfish

Evolution

1 What does *Eohippus* mean?

Answer: Dawn horse

2 How many toes did *Eohippus* have?

Answer: Four

3 A horse's hoof is used for swimming. True or false?

Answer: False, it is used for running

4 When did the last dinosaurs die out?

Answer: 65 million years ago

5 How do we know about dinosaurs?

Answer: From their fossils

6 Who explained how evolution works?

Answer: Charles Darwin

7 Where was Charles Darwin from?

Answer: England

8 Why are animals all slightly different from each other?

Answer: Because of evolution

Water for life

1 Why is extra water put on some crops?

Answer: To help them grow

2 Rice fields are called paddies. True or false?

Answer: True

3 Re-arrange RSRVOREEI for a place where we store water.

Answer: RESERVOIR

4 How are reservoirs made?

Answer: By building a dam across a river

5 Where do canals and pipes take water to?

Answer: Farms and cities

6 Where can you find clean water?

Answer: Deep underground

7 Where does a bottle tree grow?

Answer: In Australia and also Africa

8 Where does a bottle tree store its water?

Answer: In its thick trunk

Harming the planet

1 Where does most of our rubbish go?

Answer: Into a landfill site

2 What happens once a landfill site is full?

Answer: It is covered in soil

3 Why are some forests getting smaller?

Answer: Their trees are being cut down faster than they can grow back

4 Re-arrange LLOPUTION to spell dangerous chemicals.

Answer: POLLUTION

5 Where does pollution go?

Answer: Into water and air

6 Where does oil come from?

Answer: Under the ground

7 Spilt oil is called a slick. True or false?

Answer: True

8 How do people save animals hurt by oil slicks?

Answer: They clean off the oil

Clean energy

1 How do turbines catch the wind?

Answer: With their shaped blades

2 What turns inside a wind turbine?

Answer: An electricity generator

3 What part of a generator does GNETMA spell?

Answer: MAGNET

4 Wave power helps generate energy. True or false?

Answer: True

5 Unjumble GETHMALERO.

Answer: GEOTHERMAL

6 Where does a geothermal power plant get its heat?

Answer: From deep underground

7 Semiconductors are used in solar panels. True or false?

Answer: True

8 What happens when light shines on a solar panel?

Answer: The panel produces electricity

Endangered animals

1 Where do rhinoceroses live?

Answer: In Africa and Asia

2 Why were rhinoceroses hunted?

Answer: For their horns

3 How many mountain gorillas live in the wild?

Answer: About 700

4 What do mountain gorillas eat?

Answer: Leaves, flowers and roots

5 What is the largest cat in the world?

Answer: The tiger

6 Unjumble SIAA to spell where tigers live.

Answer: ASIA

7 Where do turtles lay their eggs?

Answer: On sandy beaches

8 What are many turtle beaches used for by people?

Answer: As holiday resorts

Recycling

1 Why is it good to sort out your rubbish?

Answer: To make recycling easier

2 Unjumble COSOTPM.

Answer: COMPOST

3 What can you compost at home?

Answer: Fruit and vegetables

4 What happens at a recycling plant?

Answer: Rubbish is sorted into different types of material

5 What pulls metals out of mixed-up rubbish?

Answer: Magnets

6 Paper is separated from rubbish with a fan. True or false?

Answer: True

7 What can paper be made into?

Answer: Cardboard

8 Name something that can be made from plastic bottles.

Answer: A chair or jacket

Helping save the planet

1 What could help save our planet?

Answer: New technology

2 What do cleaner cars run on?

Answer: Hydrogen or electricity

3 What is conservation?

Answer: Protecting rare wildlife

4 Unjumble DAPNA for a giant, rare animal.

Answer: PANDA

5 Name a charity that works to save rare animals.

Answer: World Wildlife Fund (WWF)

6 World leaders and scientists meet to fix which problem?

Answer: Climate change

7 What could you do to help save the planet?

Answer: Walk or use a bicycle

8 Is it better to get food grown near home or far away?

Answer: Close to where you live

Index

Acknowledgements

The publisher would like to thank the following for permission to reproduce their photographs. Every care has been taken to trace copyright holders. However, if there have been unintentional omissions or failure to trace copyright holders, we apologize and will, if informed, endeavour to make corrections in any future edition.

Page: 12 (bottom) Stephen Lings; 13 Shutterstock/ (right) Dennis Donohue, (bottom) Jeff Grabert; 14 Shutterstock/ Boris Stroujko; 15 (top) Shutterstock/Jeremy Richards; 17 (top) Shutterstock/ (top) Andreas Gradin (right) Vaclav Volrab; 18 Shutterstock/Pichugin Dmitry; 19 Shutterstock/Guido Vrola; 29 (top) Stephen Lings; 31 Shutterstock/ Rich Carey; 38 Shutterstock/Kristian Sekulic; 39 (top) Sebastian Quigley; 40 Shutterstock/javarman; 41 (top) Shutterstock/Ryan Rodrick Beiler (bottom) GettyImages/AFP/Ramzi Haidar; 43 (bottom) Shutterstock/Thomas Hruschka; 45 Shutterstock/Marc van Vuren; 47 Shutterstock/Tatiana Grozetskaya; 49 (top) (bottom) Shutterstock/ Sergei Butorin; 50 Shutterstock/Gail Johnson; 51 (bottom) Shutterstock/Stanislaff; 53 Shutterstock/ (top) Ramon Berk (bottom) pinecone; 54 Shutterstock/Dark o; 54 Shutterstock/ (top) jam4travel (right) Stephen Finn; 57 Shutterstock/ Lockenes; 59 (top) Shutterstock/Ozerov Alexander; 60 Shutterstock/AndreiC; 61 (top) Shutterstock/Sascha Burkard; 67 Shutterstock/ (top) Jeff Martinez (right) Glovatskiy; 68 Reuters/Ho New; 69 Getty Images/AFP; 73 (middle) Sebastian Quigley; 77 (top) Shutterstock/Inacio Pires (middle) Corbis/Gideon Mendel (bottom) Sebastian Quigley; 80 Shutterstock/Insuratelu G Gianina; 81 (bottom) Shutterstock/Joe Gough; 83 (top) Shutterstock/Sam Chadwick; 86 Shutterstock; 87 (right) Shutterstock/Monkey Business Images (bottom) Reuters/Larry Downing.